I love my teacher

Giles Andreae & Emma Dodd

ORCHARD

Quick, let's go!

It's time for school!

My teachers there

are pretty cool.

They smile at me and say hello.

"Bye now, Mummy, you can go!"

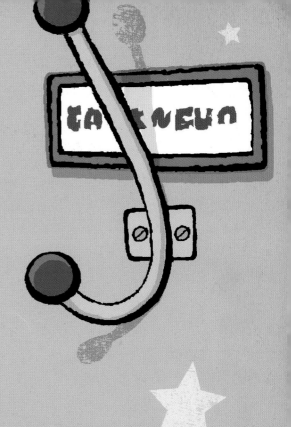

I hang my coat up
on my hook.
It's got my name on –
take a look!

I find my friends

and play some games

Before my teacher

calls our names.

She asks about the things we've done. We show and tell – it's lots of fun!

We do some writing . . .

numbers too,

'Cause learning stuff

is good for you.

And sometimes when

I read out loud

My teacher says

she's very proud!

When break time comes, we run outside.

Who'll be the first
one down the slide?

We go back in to paint and draw,

Then stick our pictures on the door.

We make a lot of things as well.

This one's my favourite! Can you tell?

My teacher helps us sing a song . . .

It's home time now, so coats back on.

"What fun we've had!" I hear her say,

"Tomorrow is another day . . . "

She's clever and
she's smart, that's true.
But, most of all . . .

she's lovely too!